GW00400039

BoE 4483

Hans-Günter Heumann

THE VERY BEST OF...

ABBA

Die größten Hits	The Greatest Hits
der schwedischen Pop-Gruppe	Of The Swedish Pop Band
in leichten Arrangements	In Easy Arrangements
für Klavier	For Piano

Inhalt/Contents

Extra-Beilage: Alle Texte der Songs

BOSWORTH EDITION

B. & Co. 25 604

Waterloo

Words & Music by Benny Andersson, Björn Ulvaeus & Stig Anderson
Arr.: Hans-Günter Heumann

B. & Co. 25 604

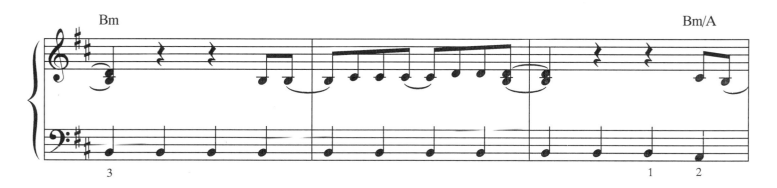

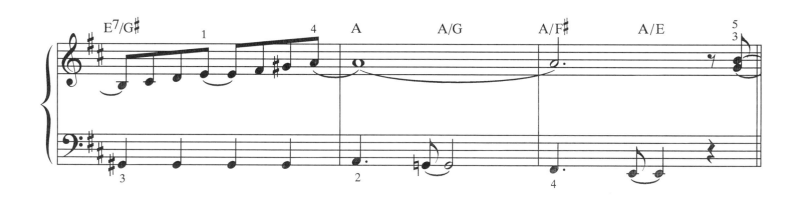

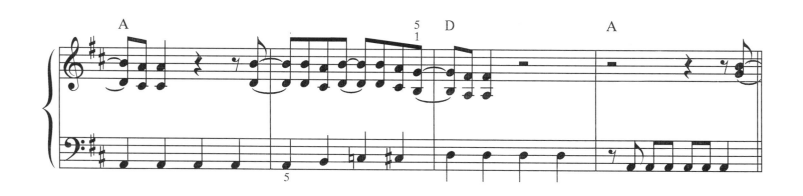

4

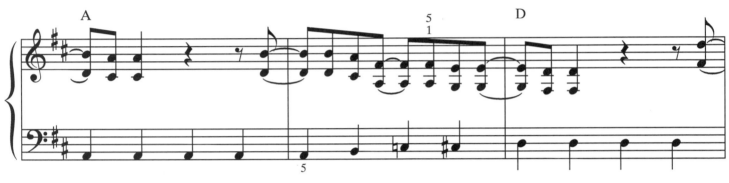

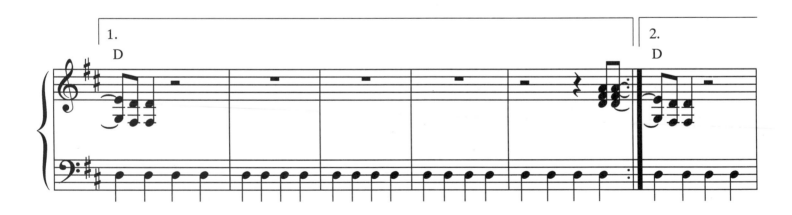

S. O. S.

Words & Music by Benny Andersson, Björn Ulvaeus & Stig Anderson
Arr.: Hans-Günter Heumann

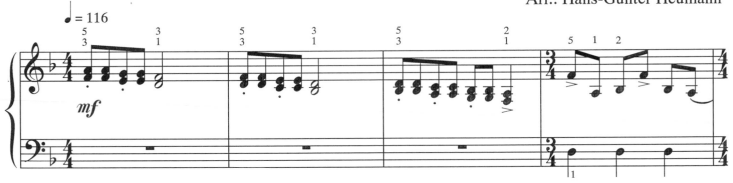

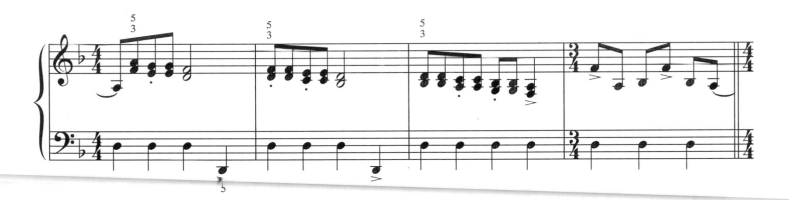

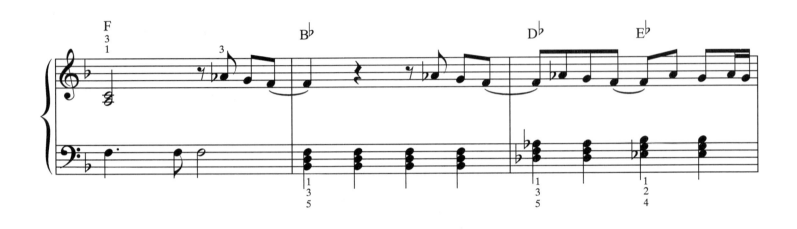

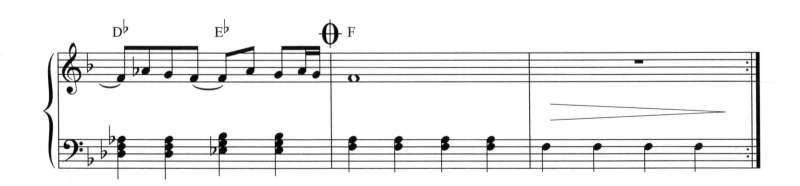

Mamma Mia

Words & Music by Benny Andersson, Björn Ulvaeus & Stig Anderson
Arr.: Hans-Günter Heumann

B. & Co. 25 604

13

B. & Co. 25 604

Dancing Queen

Words & Music by Benny Andersson, Björn Ulvaeus & Stig Anderson
Arr.: Hans-Günter Heumann

B. & Co. 25 604

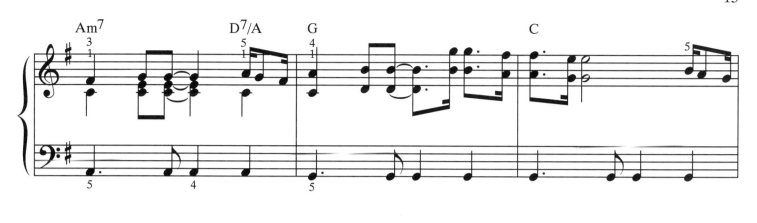

Money, Money, Money

Words & Music by Benny Andersson & Björn Ulvaeus
Arr.: Hans-Günter Heumann

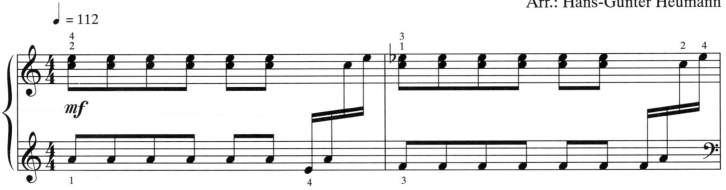

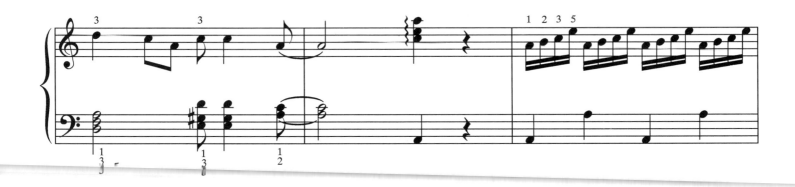

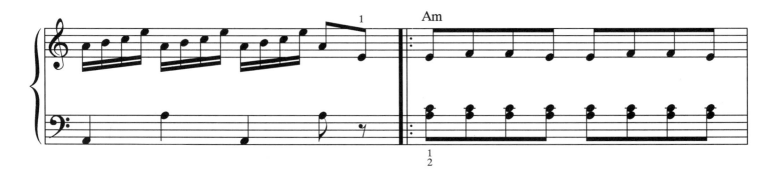

B. & Co. 25 604

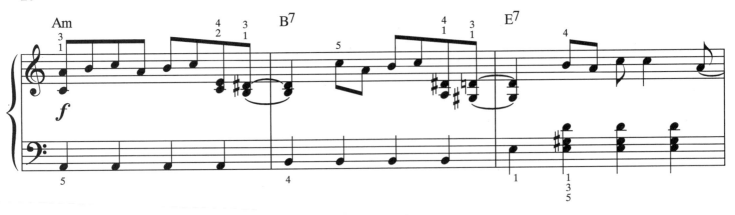

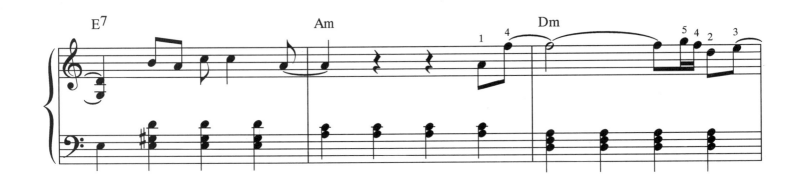

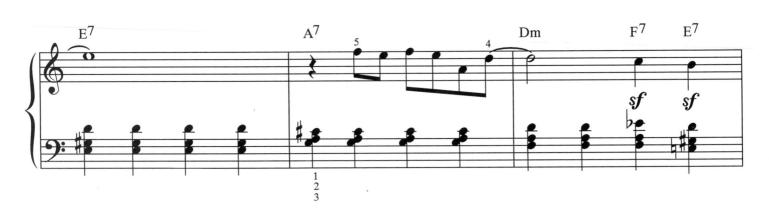

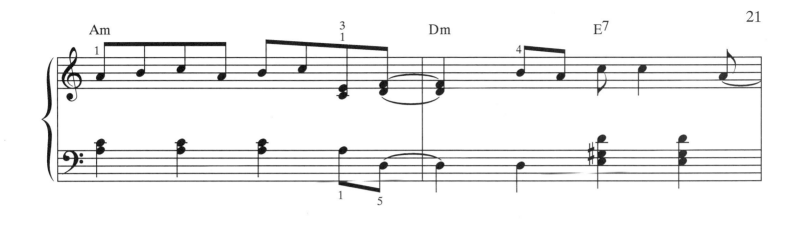

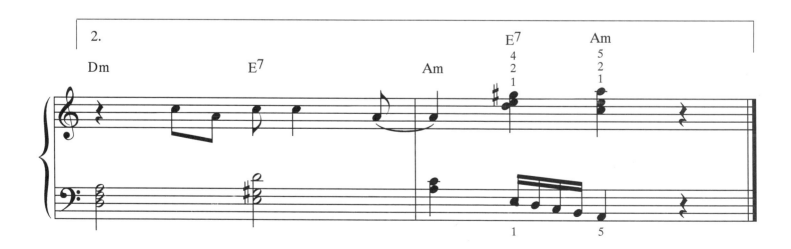

Fernando

Words & Music by Benny Andersson & Björn Ulvaeus & Stig Anderson
Arr.: Hans-Günter Heumann

B. & Co. 25 604

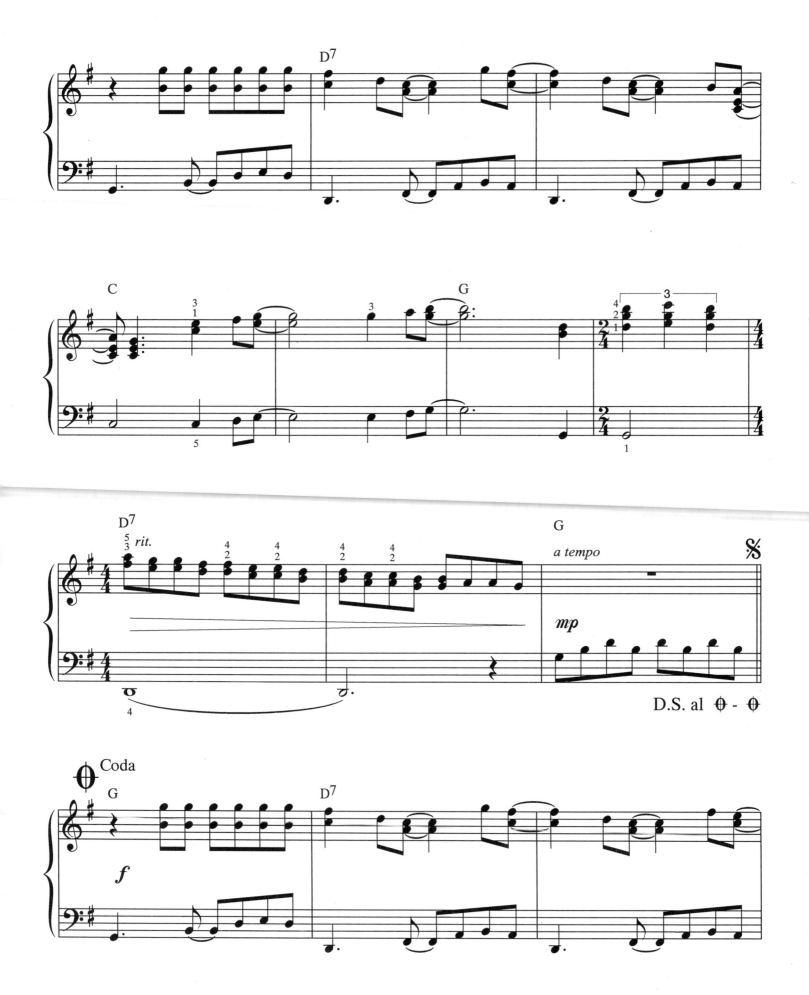

Thank You For The Music

Words & Music by Benny Andersson & Björn Ulvaeus
Arr.: Hans-Günter Heumann

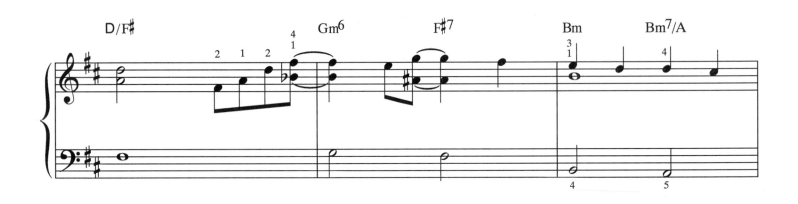

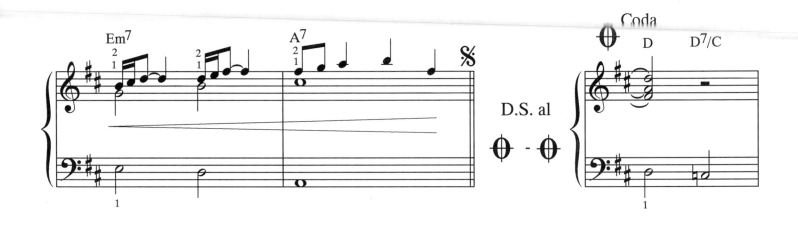

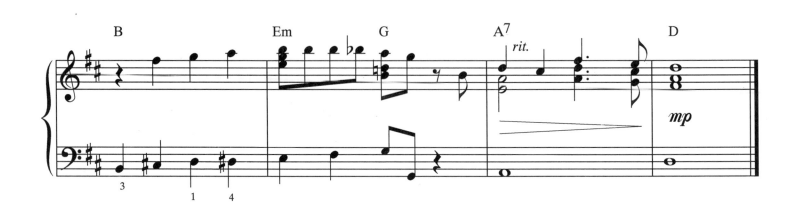

Take A Chance On Me

Words & Music by Benny Andersson & Björn Ulvaeus
Arr.: Hans-Günter Heumann

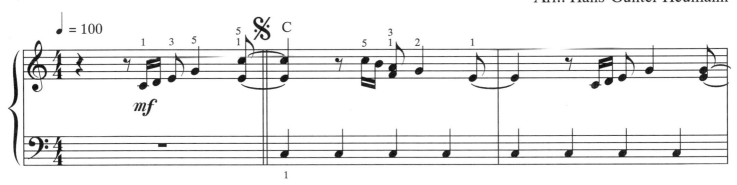

B. & Co. 25 604

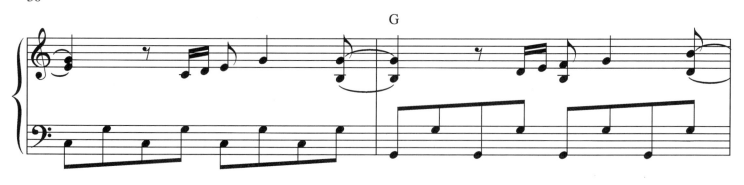

I Have A Dream

Words & Music Benny Andersson & Björn Ulvaeus
Arr.: Hans-Günter Heumann

B. & Co. 25 604

The Winner Takes It All

Words & Music by Benny Andersson & Björn Ulvaeus
Arr.: Hans-Günter Heumann

B. & Co. 25 604

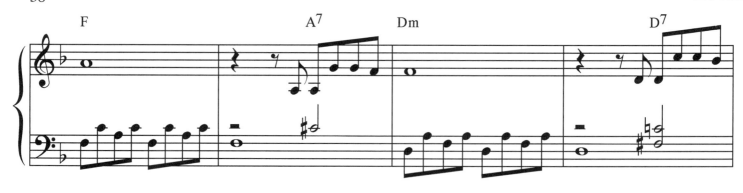

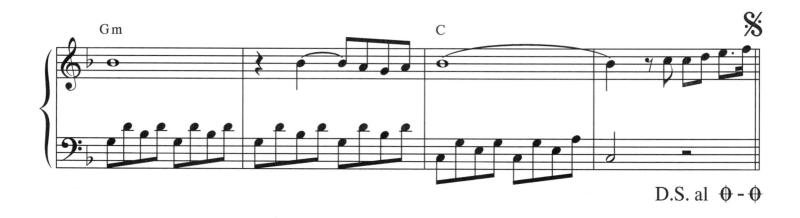

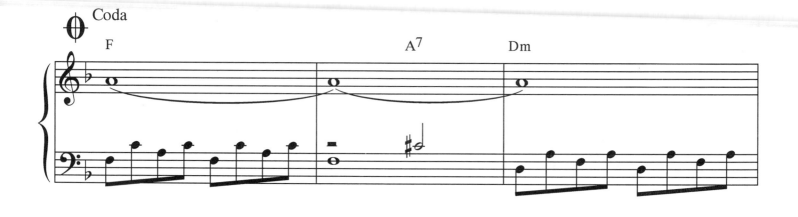

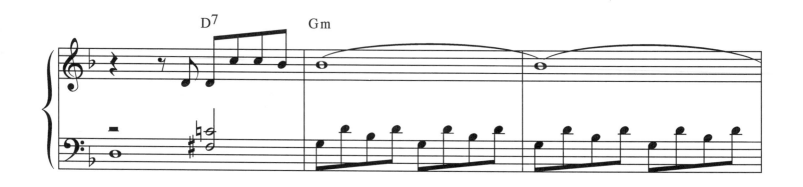

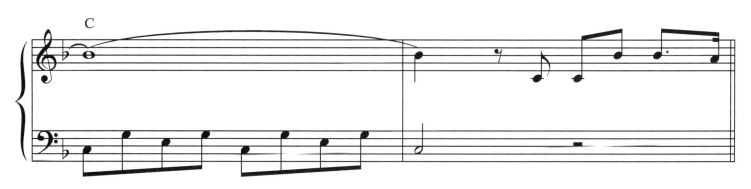

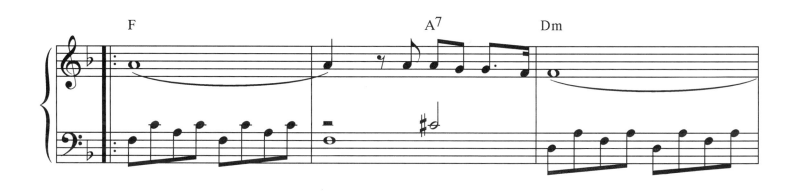

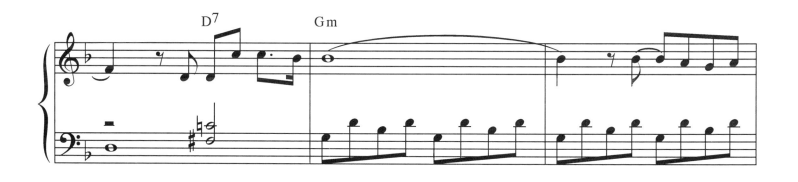

Super Trouper

Words & Music by Benny Andersson & Björn Ulvaeus
Arr.: Hans-Günter Heumann

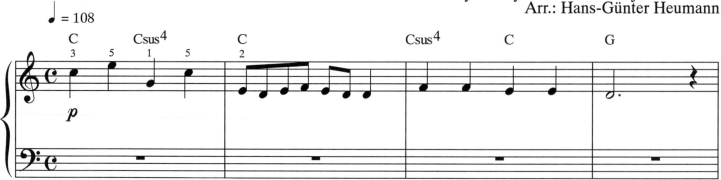

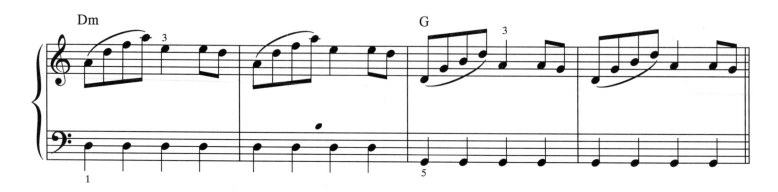

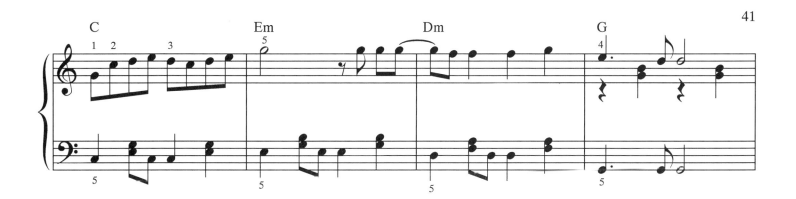

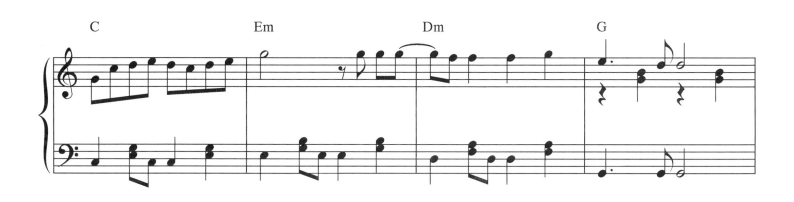

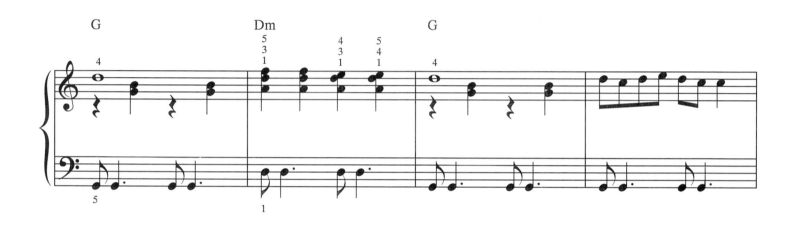

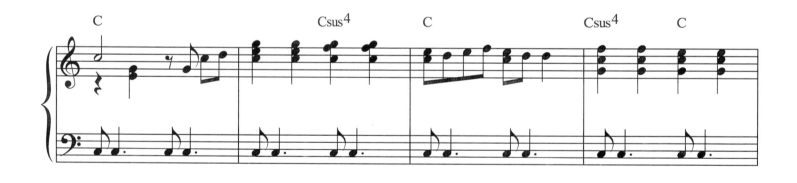

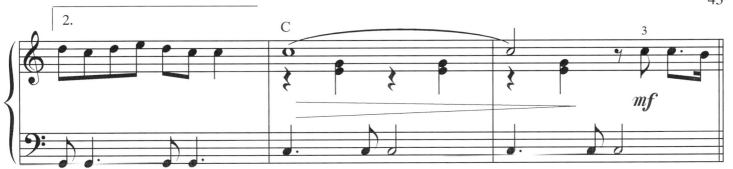

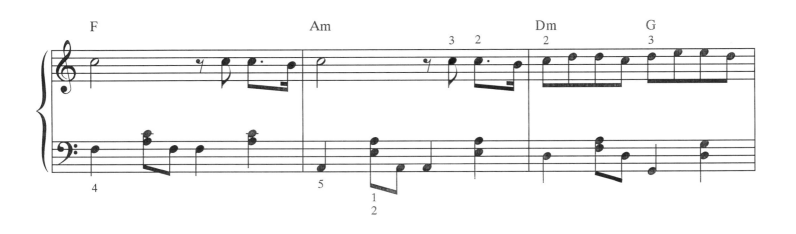

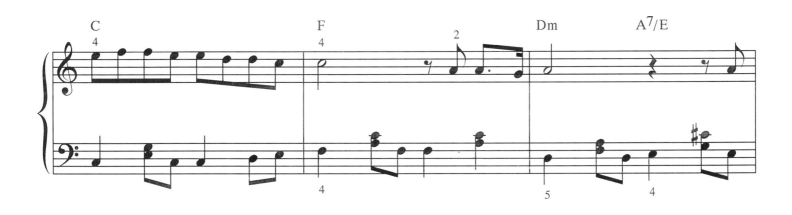

D.S. al ⊕ - ⊕

Lay All Your Love On Me

Words & Music by Benny Andersson & Björn Ulvaeus
Arr.: Hans-Günter Heumann

45

B. & Co. 25 604

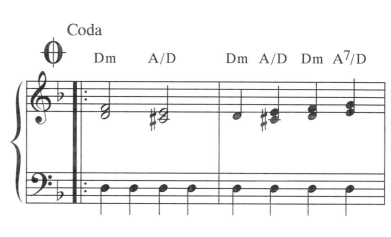

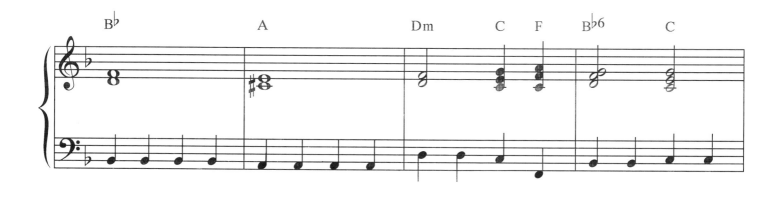

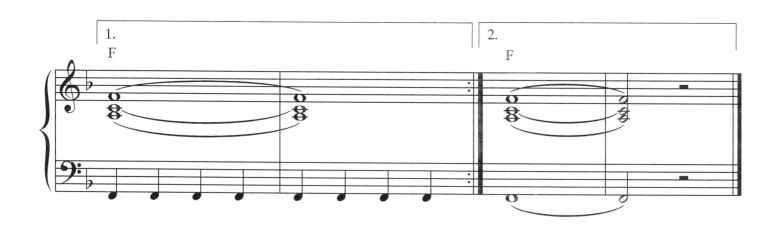

Made in the EU   9/03 (48504)